Over The Rainbow

Very Best Of Judy Garland

© 2010 by Faber Music Ltd
First published by Faber Music Ltd in 2010
Bloomsbury House 74–77 Great Russell Street London WC1B 3DA

New Arrangements by Olly Weeks
Edited by Lucy Holliday & Alex Davis

Designed by Lydia Merrills-Ashcroft
Photos © Maurizio Tattoni & Michael Ochs Archives & Getty Images

Printed in England by Caligraving Ltd

The text paper used in this publication is a virgin fibre product that is manufactured in the EU.
The wood fibre used is only sourced from managed forests using sustainable forestry principles.
This paper is 100% recyclable

ISBN10: 0-571-53562-3
EAN13: 978-0-571-53562-0

To buy Faber Music publications or to find out about the full range of titles available,
please contact your local music retailer or Faber Music sales enquiries:
Faber Music Ltd, Burnt Mill, Elizabeth Way, Harlow, CM20 2HX England
Tel: +44(0)1279 82 89 82 Fax: +44(0)1279 82 89 83
sales@fabermusic.com fabermusic.com

OVER THE RAINBOW
(FROM "THE WIZARD OF OZ")

Music by Harold Arlen
Lyrics by E. Y. Harburg

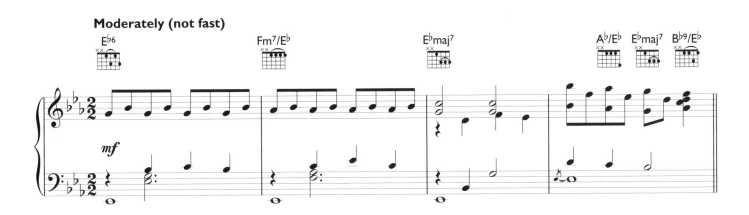

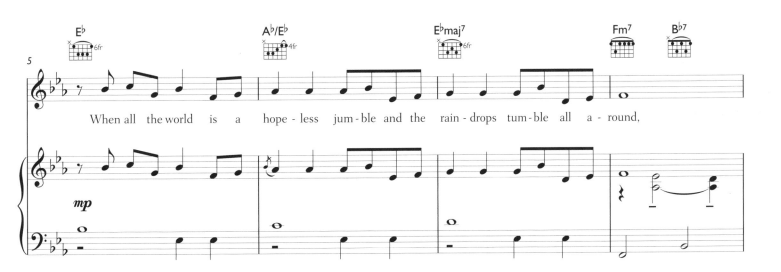

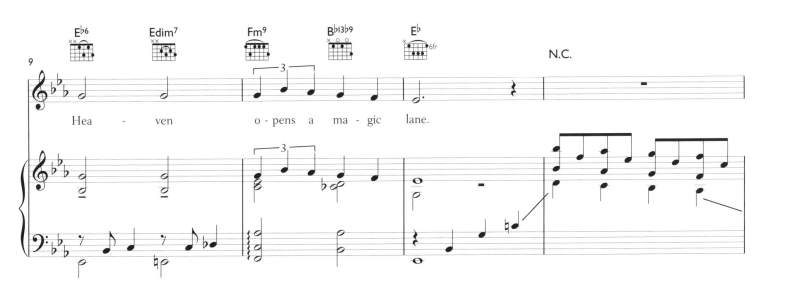

4

STOMPIN' AT THE SAVOY

Words by Andy Razaf
Music by Benny Goodman, Edgar Sampson and Chick Webb

MR GABLE, YOU MADE ME LOVE YOU

Words by Joe McCarthy Sr
Music by James V Monaco

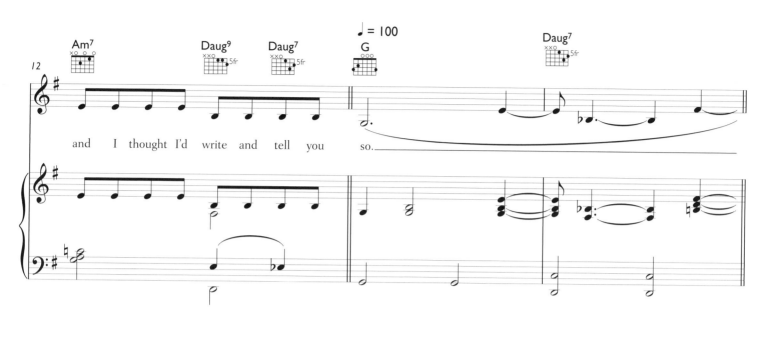

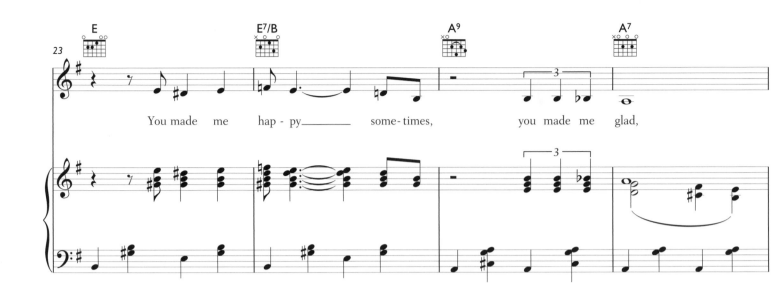

You made me hap-py_____ some-times, you made me glad,

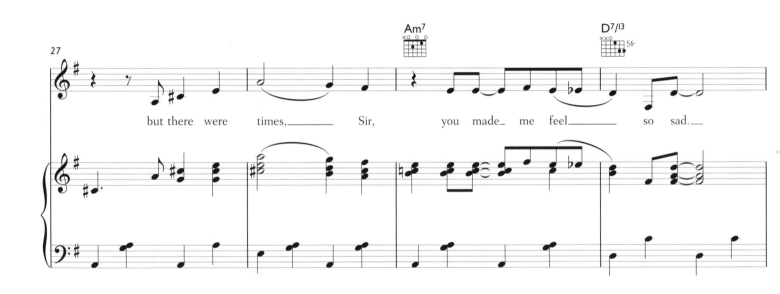

but there were times,_____ Sir, you made_ me feel_____ so sad._

You made me sigh 'cos I did-n't want to tell you, I did-n't want to tell you,

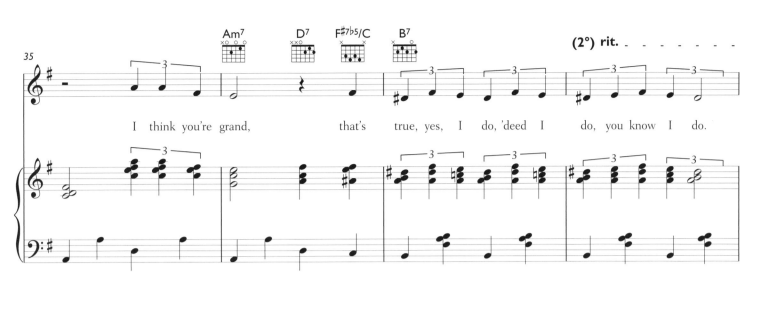

I think you're grand, that's true, yes, I do, 'deed I do, you know I do.

I must tell you what I'm feel-ing, the ve-ry men-tion of your name sends my heart reel-ing,_

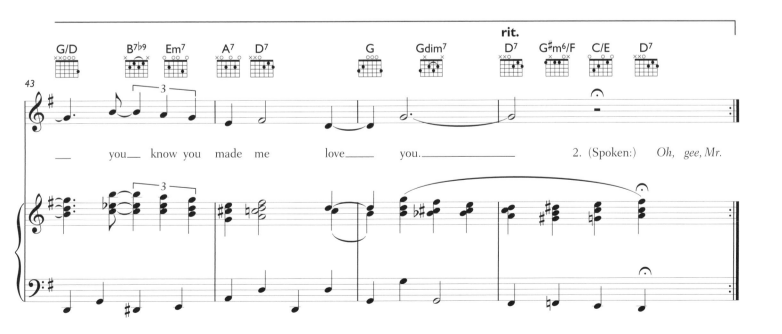

you_ know you made me love_ you._ 2. (Spoken:) *Oh, gee, Mr.*

Verse 2: *(Spoken)*

Oh gee, Mr. Gable, I don't wanna bother you - I guess you've got a lot of girls who'll tell you the same thing,

and if you don't want to read this, well, oh, you don't have to.

But I just had to tell you about the time I saw you and it happened one night,

That was the first time I ever saw you, and I knew right then you were the nicest fella in the movies.

I guess it was because you acted so, oh, so natural, like.

Oh, not like a real actor at all but just any fella you meet at school or at a party.

And then one time I saw you in a picture with Joan Crawford and I had to cry a little 'cos you loved her so much

and you couldn't have her - well, not 'til the end of the picture anyway.

And then one time I saw you in person; you were going to the Coconut Grove one night

and I was standing there when you got out of your car and you almost knocked me down!

Oh, but it wasn't your fault! No, I was in the way. But you looked at me and you smiled, yes you smiled right at me as if you meant it

and I cried all the way home just 'cos you smiled at me for being in your way -

Oh, I'll never forget it, Mr. Gable, honest injun, you're my favourite actor!

ZING! WENT THE STRINGS OF MY HEART

Words and Music by James Hanley

18

I'M JUST WILD ABOUT HARRY

Words by Noble Sissle
Music by Eubie Blake

EMBRACEABLE YOU

Music and Lyrics by George Gershwin and Ira Gershwin

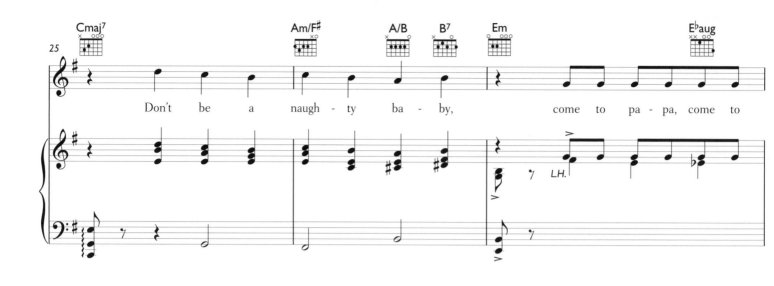

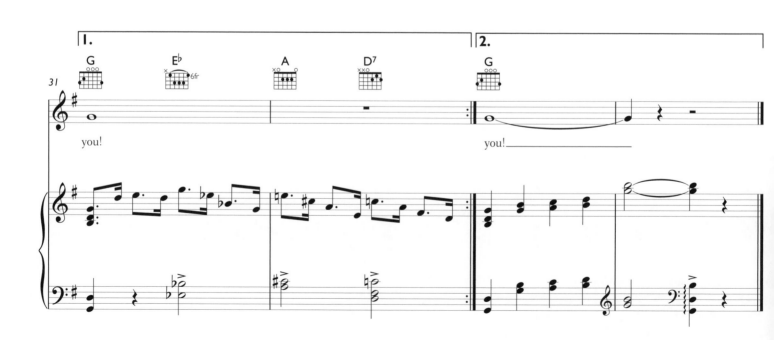

I'M NOBODY'S BABY

Words and Music by Milton Ager, Benny Davis and Lester Santly

hear my plea and take a chance with me, be-cause_ I'm_

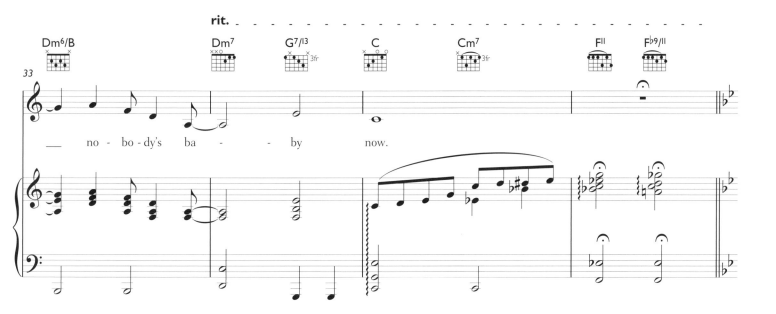

rit. _ _ _ _ _ _ _ _ _ _ _ _ _

_ no - bo - dy's ba _ _ by now.

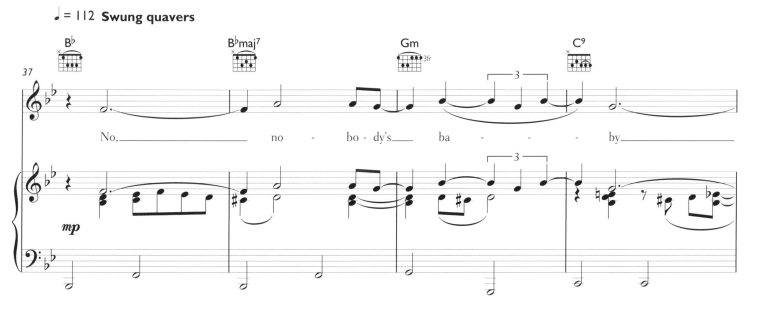

♩ = 112 **Swung quavers**

No,_____ no - bo - dy's__ ba _ _ by_____

_mp_

32

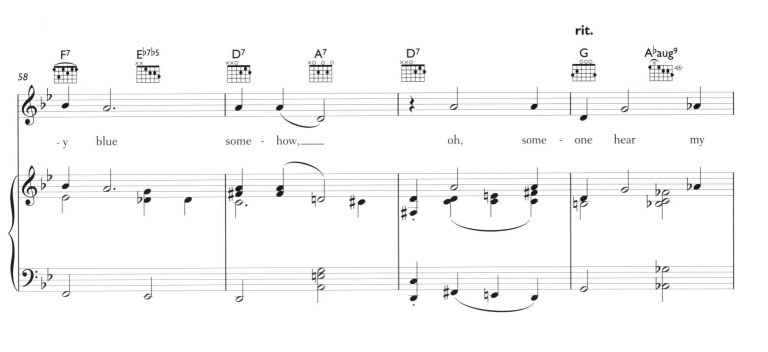

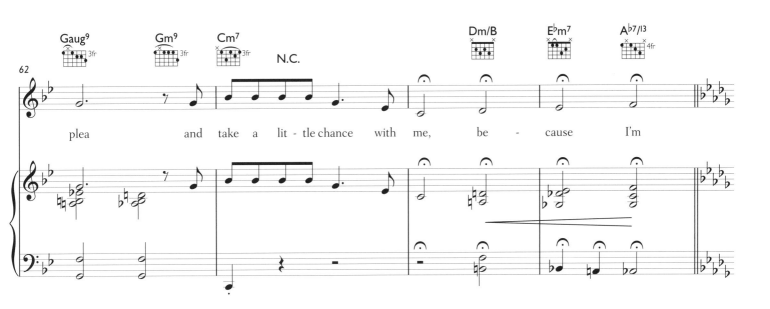

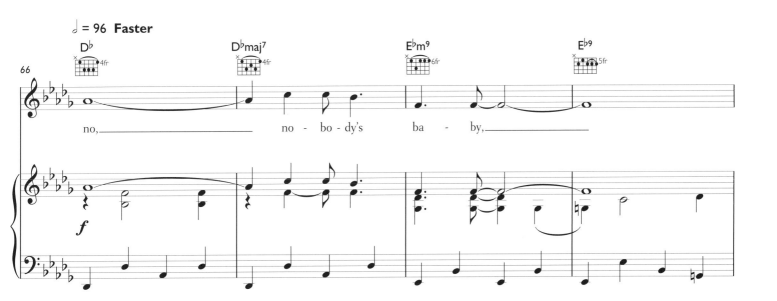

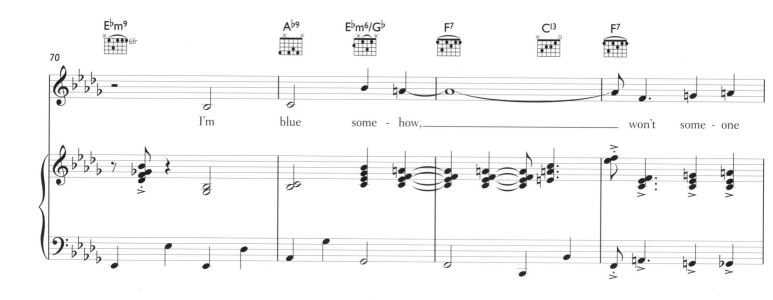

70

I'm blue some - how, _____ won't some - one

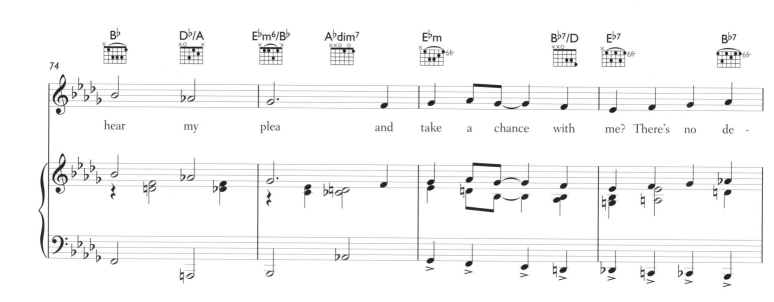

74

hear my plea and take a chance with me? There's no de -

78

- ny - ing, I'm cry - ing, I'm

SWANEE

Words by Irving Caesar
Music by George Gershwin

Moderately fast

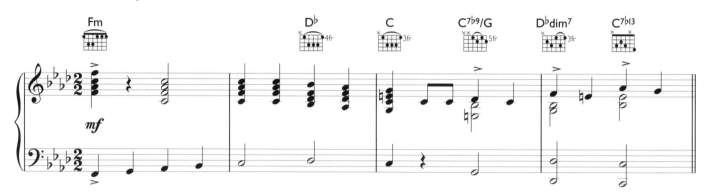

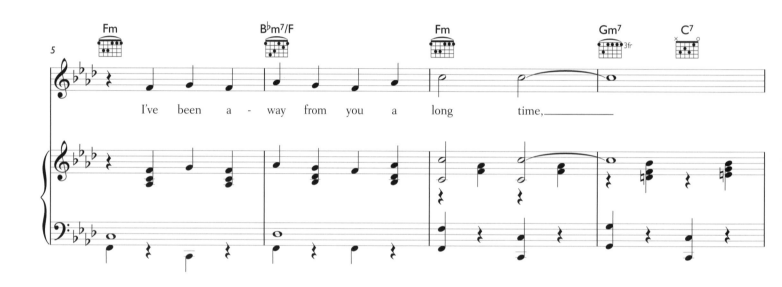

I've been a - way from you a long time,_____

I nev - er thought I'd miss you so._____

38

I'M ALWAYS CHASING RAINBOWS

Words by Joseph McCarthy
Music Arranged by Harry Carroll

HOW ABOUT YOU?

Words by Ralph Freed
Music by Burton Lane

WHEN YOU WORE A TULIP AND I WORE A BIG RED ROSE

Words by Jack Mahoney
Music by Percy Wenrich

51

BLUES IN THE NIGHT

Words by Johnny Mercer
Music by Harold Arlen

My ma-ma done tol' me____ when I was in pig - tails,_____ my ma-ma done tol' me:

"Hon,_____ a man's gon - na sweet talk____ and give you the big eye,____

blues_____ in the night._____ Mmm,_____ mmm._

My mom - my was right,____ there's blues_____ in_____ the

night._____

ON THE SUNNY SIDE OF THE STREET

Words and Music by Dorothy Fields and Jimmy McHugh

Walked with no - one and talked with no - one, and I had no - thing but

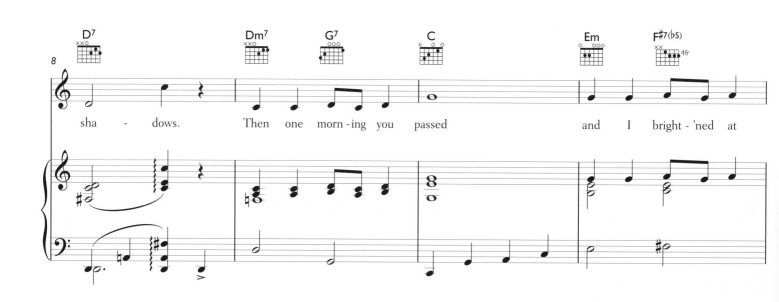

sha - dows. Then one morn - ing you passed and I bright - 'ned at

FOR ME AND MY GAL

Words by Edgar Leslie and Ray Goetz
Music by George Meyer

I'm goin' to build a lit - tle home for two,___ for three or four___ or

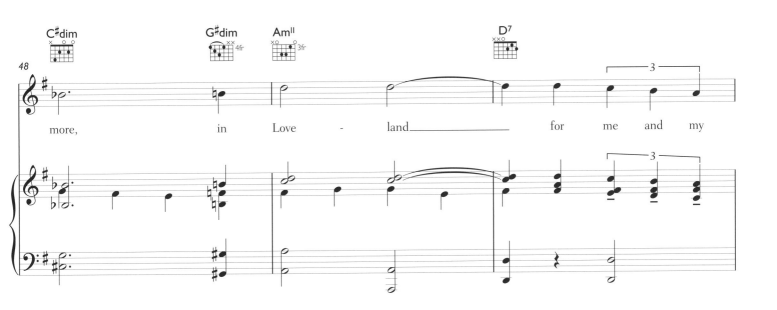

more, in Love - land___ for me and my

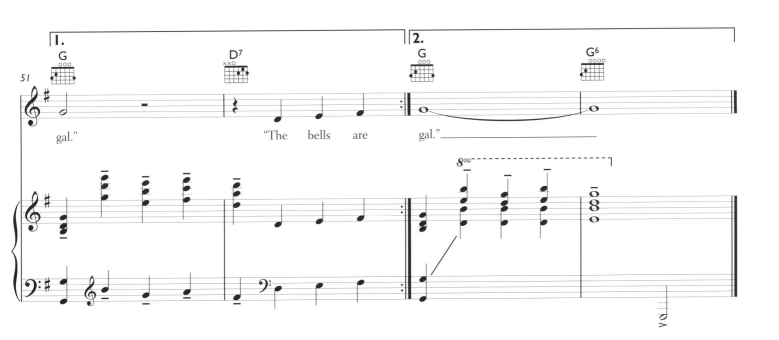

gal." "The bells are gal."_____

THAT OLD BLACK MAGIC

Words by Johnny Mercer
Music by Harold Arlen

BUT NOT FOR ME

Music and Lyrics by George Gershwin and Ira Gershwin

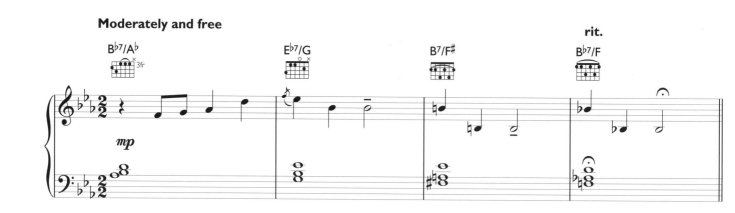

I GOT RHYTHM

Music and Lyrics by George Gershwin and Ira Gershwin

THE BOY NEXT DOOR

Words and Music by Hugh Martin and Ralph Blane

THE TROLLEY SONG

Words and Music by Ralph Blane and Hugh Martin

HAVE YOURSELF A
MERRY LITTLE CHRISTMAS

Words and Music by Hugh Martin and Ralph Blane

LOVE

Words and Music by Hugh Martin and Ralph Blane

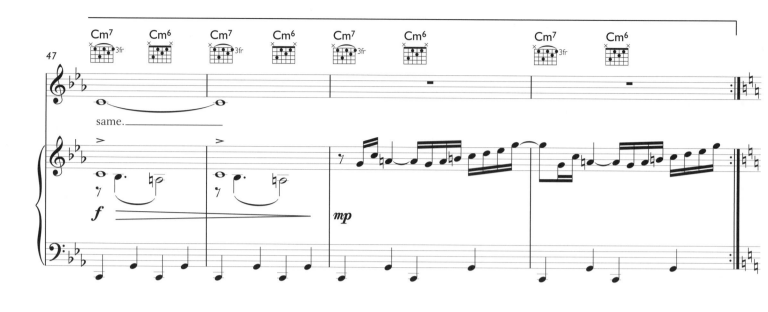

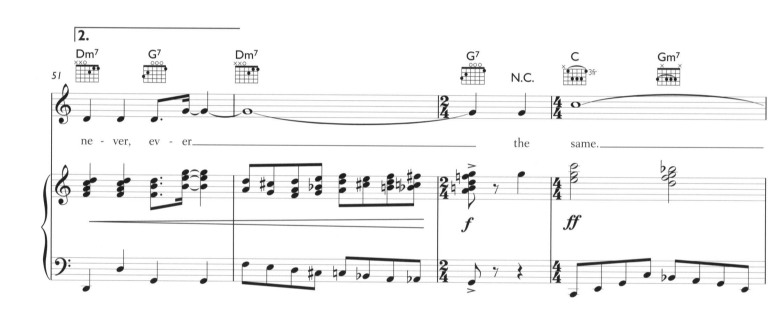

YOU'LL NEVER WALK ALONE
(FROM "CAROUSEL")

Lyrics by Oscar Hammerstein II
Music by Richard Rodgers

hope in your heart, and you'll ne - ver walk a -

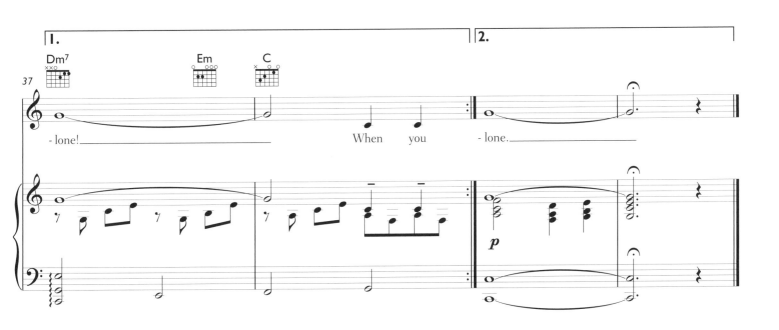

- lone,_____ you'll ne - ver walk a -

1.

- lone!_____ When you

2.

- lone._____

ON THE ATCHISON, TOPEKA AND THE SANTA FE

Words by Johnny Mercer
Music by Harry Warren

LOOK FOR THE SILVER LINING

Words by Buddy De Sylva
Music by Jerome Kern

1. Look for the sil-ver lin-ing when-e'er a cloud ap-pears in the blue. Re-mem-ber some-where the sun is shin-ing and so the right thing to do is make it

2° instrumental, with ad lib. vocals till *

A COUPLE OF SWELLS

Words and Music by Irving Berlin

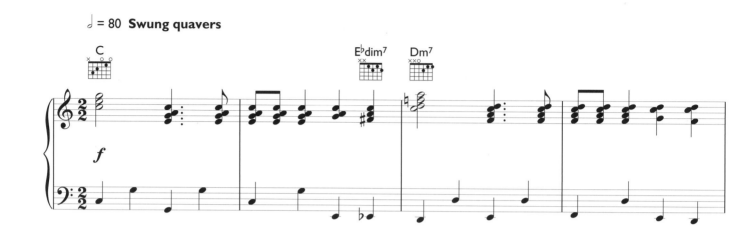

1. We're a coup-le of swells, we stop at the best ho-tels, but
2. Wall Street bank-ers are we, with plenty of___ cur-ren-cy, we'd

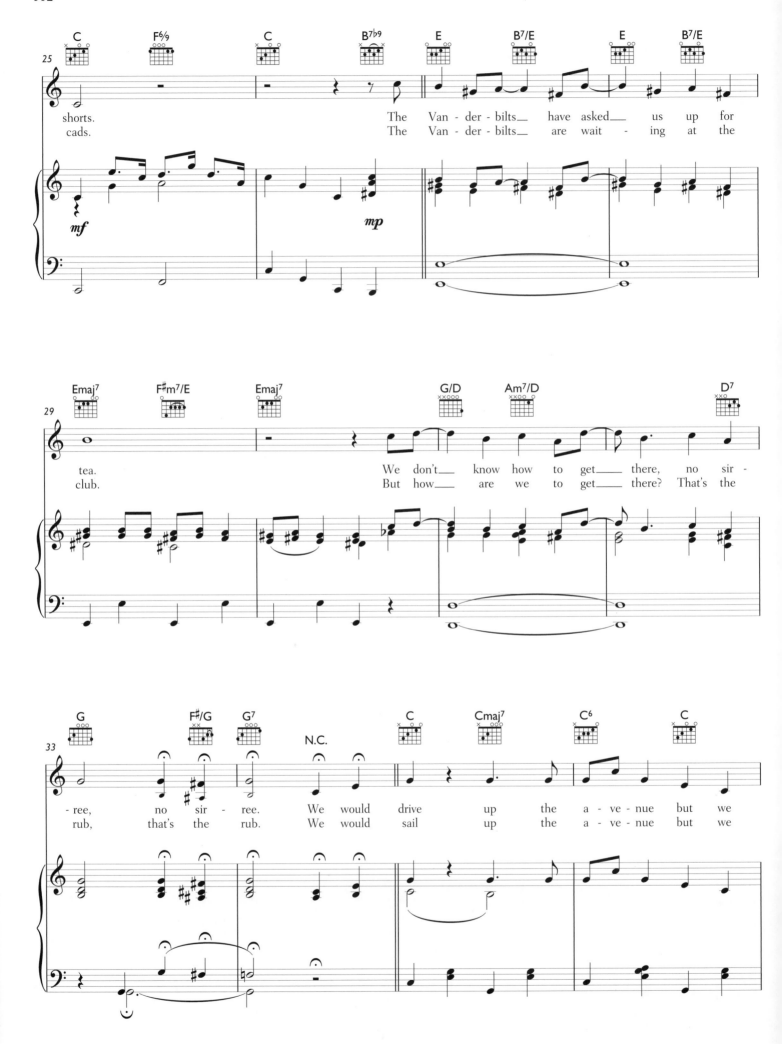

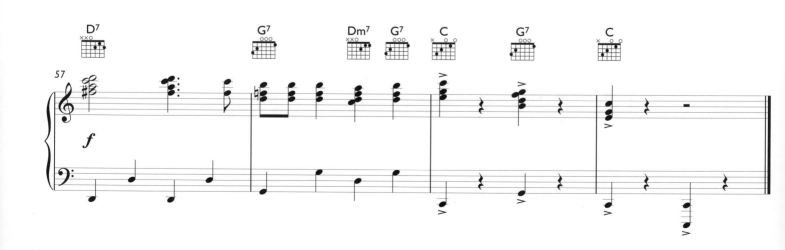

GET HAPPY

Words and Music by Harold Arlen and Ted Koehler

(CAN THIS BE) THE END OF THE RAINBOW

Words and Music by Sammy Cahn and Saul Chaplin